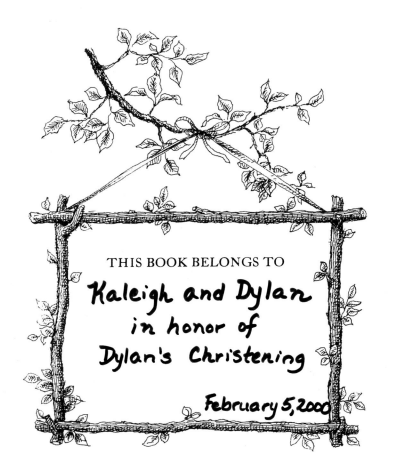

THIS BOOK BELONGS TO

Kaleigh and Dylan
in honor of
Dylan's Christening

February 5, 2000

Gyo Fujikawa's A TO Z PICTURE BOOK

BARNES
&NOBLE
BOOKS
NEW YORK

1999 Barnes & Noble Books

ISBN 0-7607-1586-6

Printed in China

99 00 01 02 03 MC 9 8 7 6 5 4 3 2 1

LFA

Acorn

Alligator

Anchor

Amaryllis

Automobile

Argument

Airplane

Artist

Anger

Agreement

Eat an apple going to bed—
make the doctor beg his bread.

Armadillo

a

A is for alone,
      all by myself . . .
   Hi, there, frog!
Can I play with you?

Bobolink

Bashful

Bugle

Butterfly

Bow

Bonnet

Ball

Bunny

Bib

Bottle

Bell

Black eye

Boat

Bear

Banana

Boots

Blackberries

Button

Balloon

Bicycle

Boxes

Bags

Bone

Bellybutton

Bread

Barrel

Bee

Basket

Bug

Buttercup

Bed

Bye-bye

B is for busy babies!

Clover

Candy

Chipmunk

Clown

Cone

Chicken

Chicks

Cow

Crown

Chocolate Cake

Calf

Chair

Cuckoo Clock

Chickadee

Charlie is Cold

Clara is Crawling

Cat and Copy Cat

Camel

Crybaby

Crab

Cactus

Cheese

Caterpillar

C is for city!

Daisy

Dormouse

Deer

Dragonfly

Doctor

Doll

Dogs

Dachshund

Duck and Ducklings

Dove

Diver

Dolphin

Doghouse

Daffodil

David Digs

Dandelion

D is for dreams,
    all kinds of dreams,

dangerous . . .   and delicious ones . . .

dreadful . . .   delightful . . .   and disgusting ones!

E

Edelweiss

Emma cleans
her Ears

Eye

Elephant

Elf

Eskimo

Edward is Eating

Eggs

e

Frog

Fox

Furry Friends

Fishes

Figleaf

Fig

Flamingo

Forget-me-not

Feather

Fearless Freddie

F is for
    friends,
    fairies,
    flowers,
    fishes,
    and frogs.

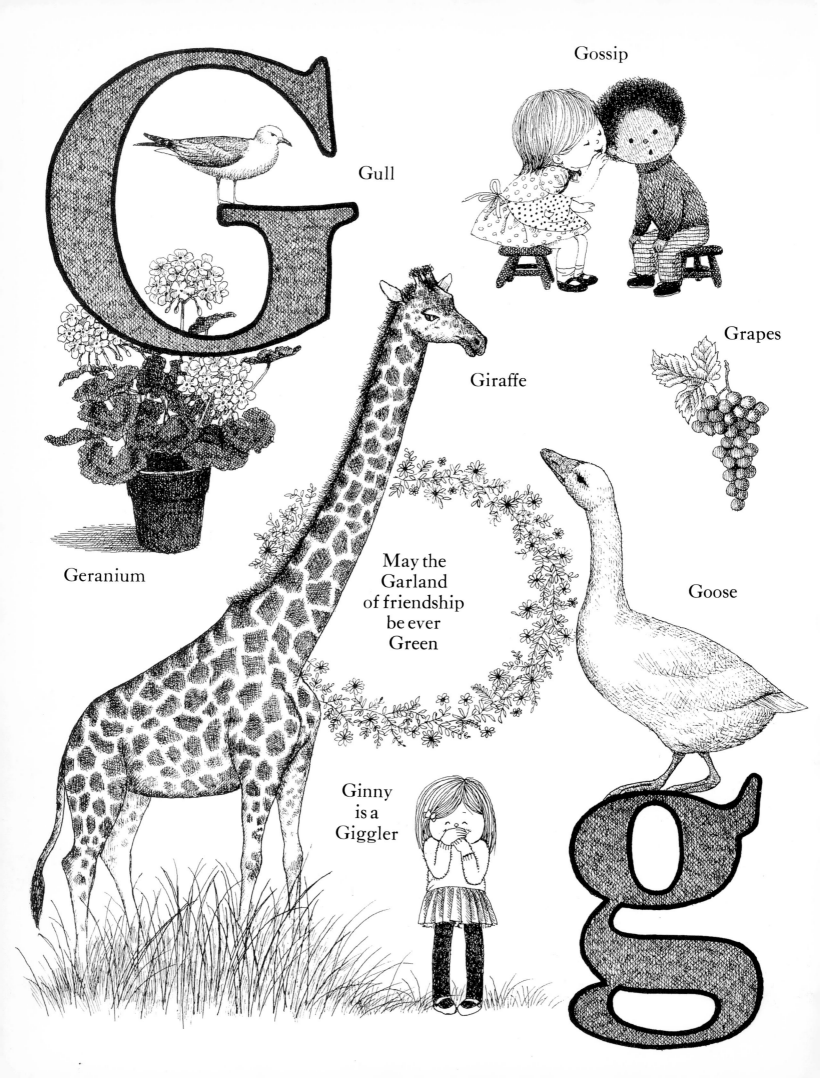

Gull

Gossip

Grapes

Giraffe

Geranium

Goose

May the
Garland
of friendship
be ever
Green

Ginny
is a
Giggler

Hummingbird

Halo

Harp

Hatchet

Hammer

House

Home Sweet Home

Hollyhocks

Horse

Henry is Hungry
for his

Harold is Happy
with his

Hamburger

Hot dog

H is for Halloween!

Icebergs

Iron

Igloo

Icing

Ibis

Iris

Ice Cream

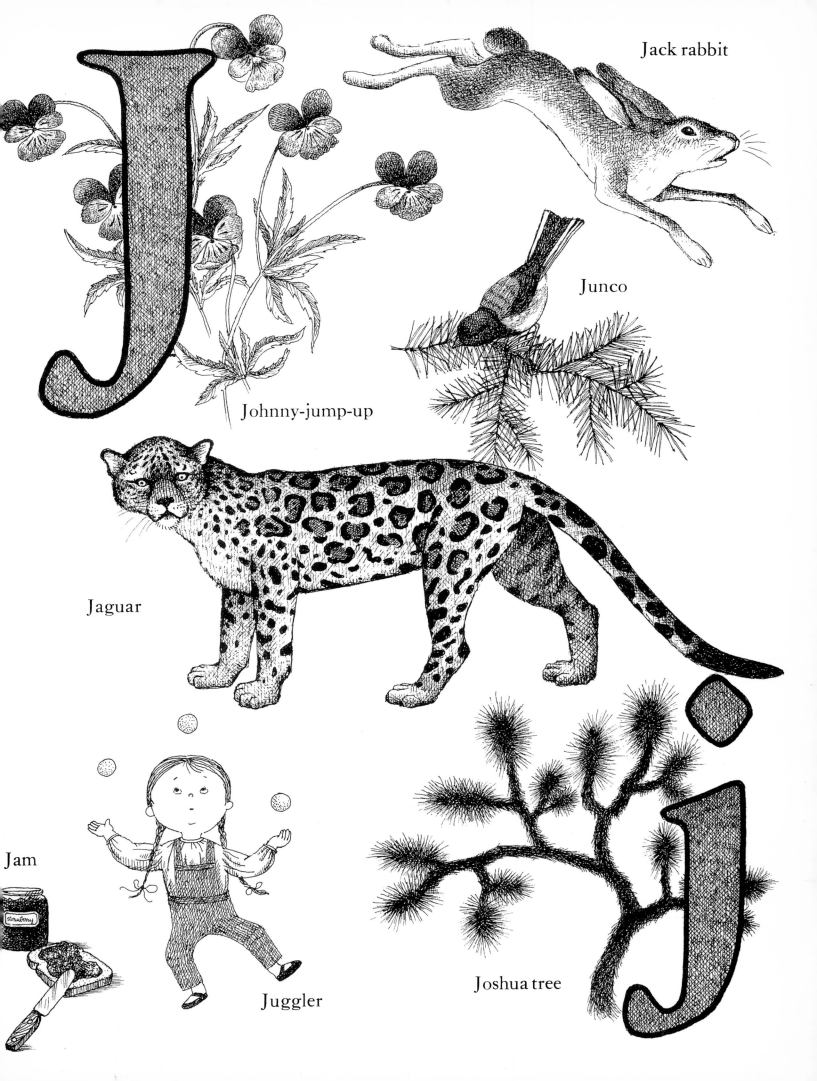

Jack rabbit

Junco

Johnny-jump-up

Jaguar

Jam

Juggler

Joshua tree

J is for
    jump,
    jump,
    jump!

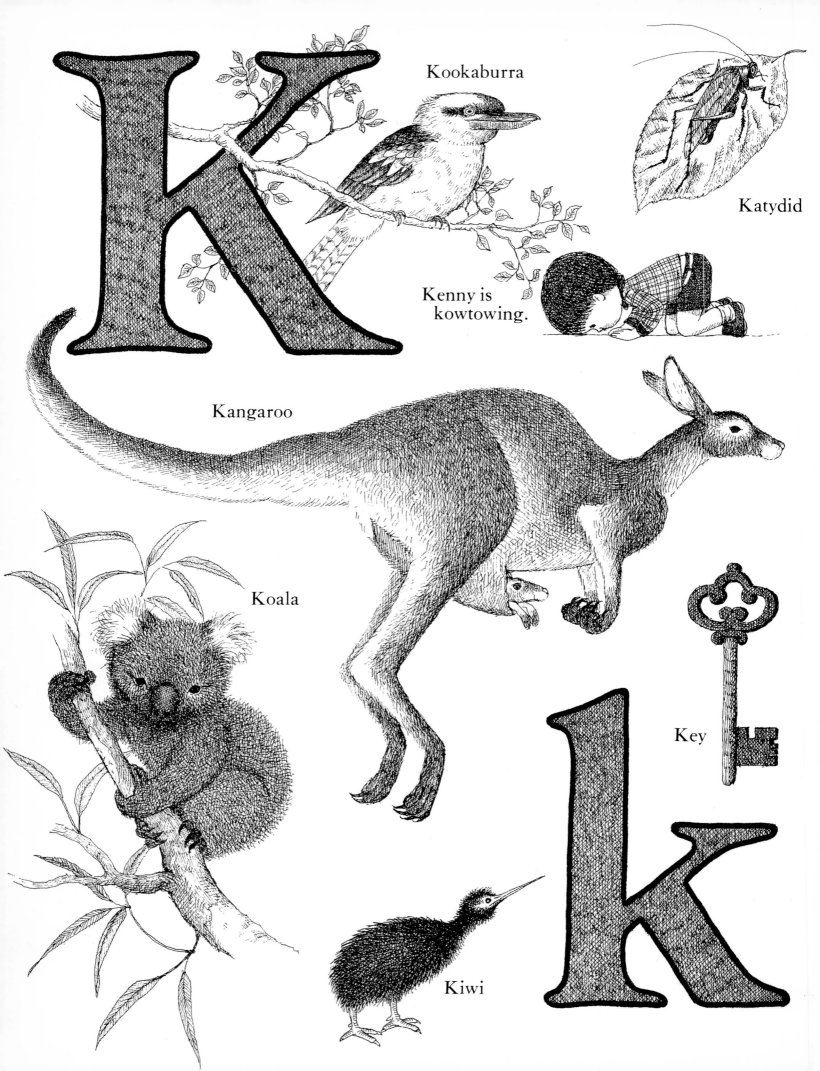

K

Kookaburra

Katydid

Kenny is
kowtowing.

Kangaroo

Koala

Key

Kiwi

k

Lark

Lobster

Lilies

Llama

Lizard

L is for lullaby,
        lions,
        lizards,
        lemons,
        and lambs.

L is for love,
        leopard,
        and lilies of the valley.

Moon

Monkey

Mountains

Mulberry

Mint

Mouse

Melon

Meow

Mitten

Muffler

Muff

Morning-glory

Moo goo gai pan

Mockingbird

Mackerel

Moose

Marigold

Milk

Mushrooms

m

M is for
my mean
and marvelous
monsters.

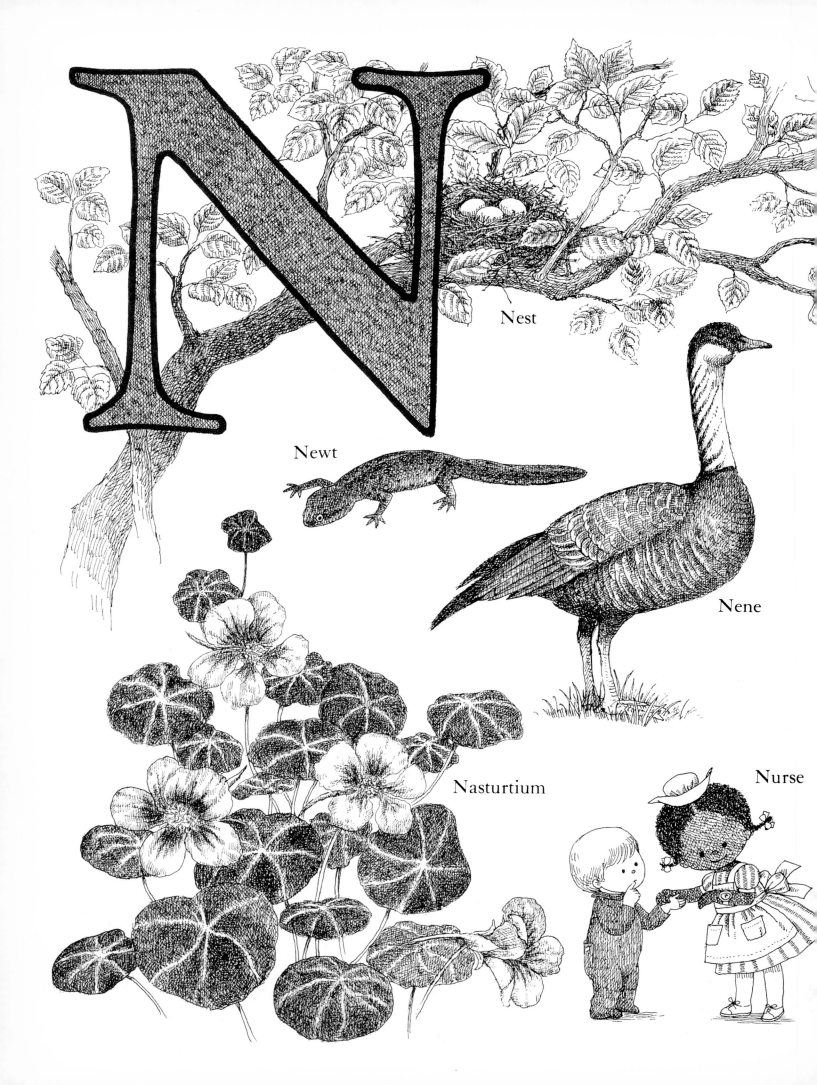

Nest

Newt

Nene

Nasturtium

Nurse

Nautilus

Necklace

Nightingale

Nuts

Nestlings

N is for numbers!

Owl

Orange

Ostrich

Octopus

Opossum

Otter

Orchid

Onions

P

Plum pudding

Parrot

Pumpkin pie

Pig

Potato

Pear

Panda

Peach

Peter pouts

Puppy

Pansies

P

P is for
pigeon,
penguin,
peacock,
puddle
and polliwogs.

Queue

Queen

Quail

Quiet!

Queen Anne's lace

Quarrel

Quill

Quintuplets

q

Robin

Rose

Raccoon

Rhinoceros

Rolling pin

Raspberries

Rat

R is for rain, rain,
        and lots more rain.
        Stop! I say—
Enough is enough!

Shower

Starfish

Swallow

Sponge

Soap

Smiling Sam swims

Sandpiper

Snake

Stuck-up

Seal

Shrimp

Swan

Sea horse

Spaghetti

Snowdrops

Shell

Sapsucker

Skunk

S is for sunflowers,
    squirrels,
    strawberries,
    and snails.

S is for black-eyed Susans,
    and spiders,
    and Sam the setter.

S is for summertime,
    sparrows,
    and snoozes
    in secret shelters.

Teardrops

Thimble

Tiger lily

Thrasher

Toothbrush   Teeth

Toothpaste   Towel

Toboggan

Tabby

Tall

Tramp

Tomato

Tough   Tender

Thanksgiving turkey

Tough   Tender

Thyme

Toad

t

Tugboat

Trumpet

Trout

T is for
topsy-turvy!

Tiger

Trees

Tepee

Taxicab

Triplets

Tulips

Thistles

Tightrope

Train

Trapeze

Tuba

Tow truck

Teddy bear

Teapot

Toucan

Teacup

Turtle

Up

Under

Ugly

Umbrella

Unicorn

Urn

Upside-down
cake

Ukulele

Unhappy

Vain

Vane

Visit

Volcano

Vaccination

Be My Valentine

Valise

Violet

Vest

Violin

V is for
vegetables.

W

Window

Woodpecker

Whale

Widgeon

Wheelbarrow

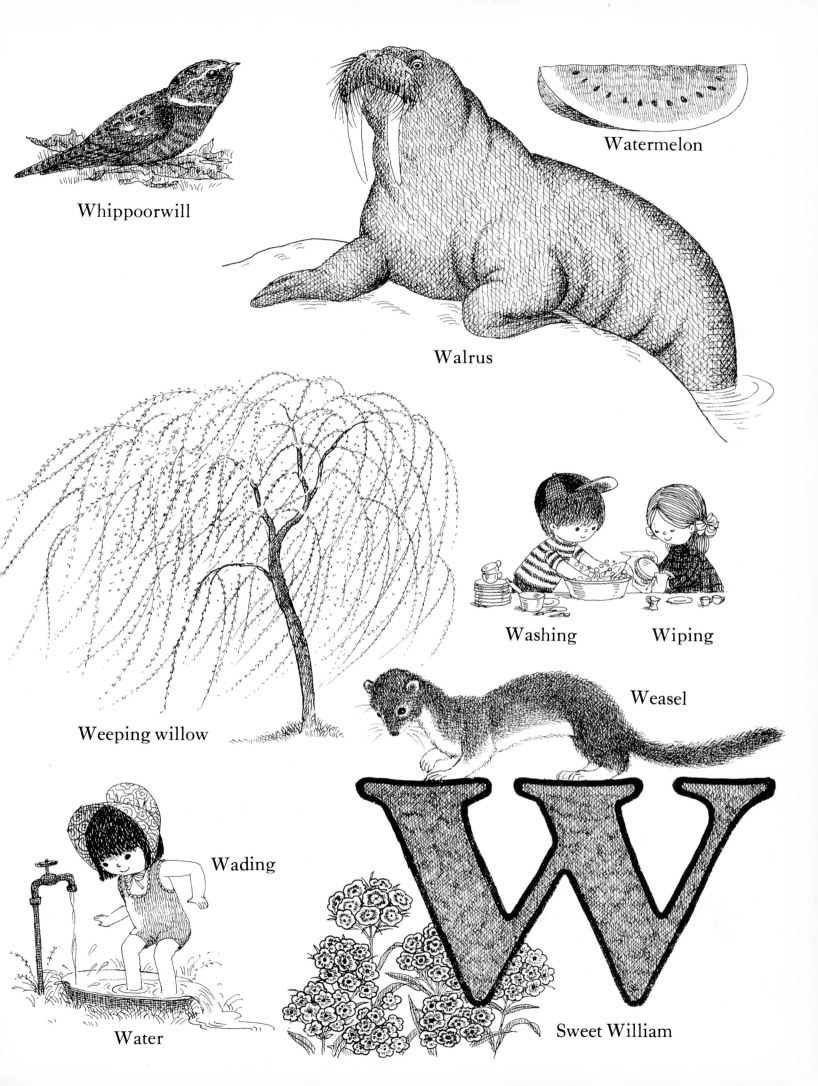

Whippoorwill

Walrus

Watermelon

Weeping willow

Washing   Wiping

Weasel

Wading

Water

Sweet William

W is for long wintertimes,
    the whistling wind,
    the winter wren,
    and the worm.

W is for the woodchuck, too,
    warm and nestled in his bed.
    How wise to sleep away the time
    until the welcome spring!

X-ray

X marks the spot.

XXXXXX is for kisses.

R X R

X is for
railroad crossing.

Xeranthemum

Xylophone

Yak

Yoo-hoo!

Yew

Yo-yo

Yellow jacket

Yacht

Yam

Yucca

Yawn

Y is for
yuletide!

Zinnia

Zombie

Zero

Zipper

Aa Bb Cc Dd
Ee Ff Gg Hh Ii
Jj Kk Ll Mm
Nn Oo Pp Qq
Rr Ss Tt Uu Vv
Ww Xx Yy Zz

Dog

Cat